Happy Birthday, Grandma!

by Anne O'Brien
illustrated by Jon Berkely

Harcourt

Orlando   Boston   Dallas   Chicago   San Diego

Visit *The Learning Site!*

www.harcourtschool.com

Here is a letter. Tina wrote the letter to her grandmother. "Happy Birthday, Grandma!" Tina wrote. Her grandmother lives far away in Florida.

Here is an envelope. Tina puts
the letter in the envelope. She
writes her grandmother's name
and address on the front. She puts
a stamp on the corner.

Here is a mailbox. Tina drops
the letter in the mailbox slot. The
mailbox keeps the letter safe and
dry until it can be picked up.

4

Here is a mail carrier. The mail carrier delivers mail to people's houses. She also picks up the letters from the mailbox and brings them to the post office.

Here is a post office. This post office is in the city where Tina lives. Mail carriers bring all the mail from all the mailboxes to the post office.

Here is a mail sorter. The mail sorter reads the address on each letter. All the letters going to one place are put together.

Here is a postmark. A machine made the postmark on Tina's letter. It shows the date and the city where the letter came from.

Here is a mail sack. After the mail is sorted, it is put into mail sacks. Each mail sack is full of letters going to the same place. This sack has mail for Florida!

Here is a mail truck. The mail sacks are placed inside the mail truck. The mail truck drives to the airport.

Here is an airplane. Some of the mail sacks are unloaded at the airport. Then they are loaded onto an airplane. One of the airplanes will fly to Florida.

Here is another mail truck. When the airplane lands in Florida, a mail truck meets it. The mail sacks will be loaded onto the mail truck.

Here is another post office. This post office is in the city where Tina's grandmother lives. The mail truck unloads the mail sacks at the post office.

Here is a mail bin. The letters are dumped out of the mail sacks into the mail bin. All the letters will be sorted again.

Here is another mail carrier. He delivers the mail to many people, including Tina's grandmother!

Here is a grandmother. She is
Tina's grandmother! She is so
happy to get a letter from Tina.
Happy Birthday, Grandma!